The Monster Chef

by Justin McCory Martin
illustrated by Mary Sullivan

SCHOLASTIC INC.

New York • Toronto • London • Auckland • Sydney
Mexico City • New Delhi • Hong Kong • Buenos Aires

Designed by Maria Lilja
ISBN-13: 978-0-545-08868-8 • ISBN-10: 0-545-08868-2
Copyright © 2009 by Scholastic Inc.
All rights reserved. Printed in China.

SCHOLASTIC, VOCABULARY TALES™, and associated logos are trademarks and/or registered trademarks of Scholastic Inc.

First printing, January 2009
12 11 10 9 8 7 6 5 4 3 2 1   9 10 11 12 13 14/0

Mr. Dibble's brand-new diner was opening tonight. There was only one problem. He had no one to cook the food. Uh-oh, he better find someone quick.

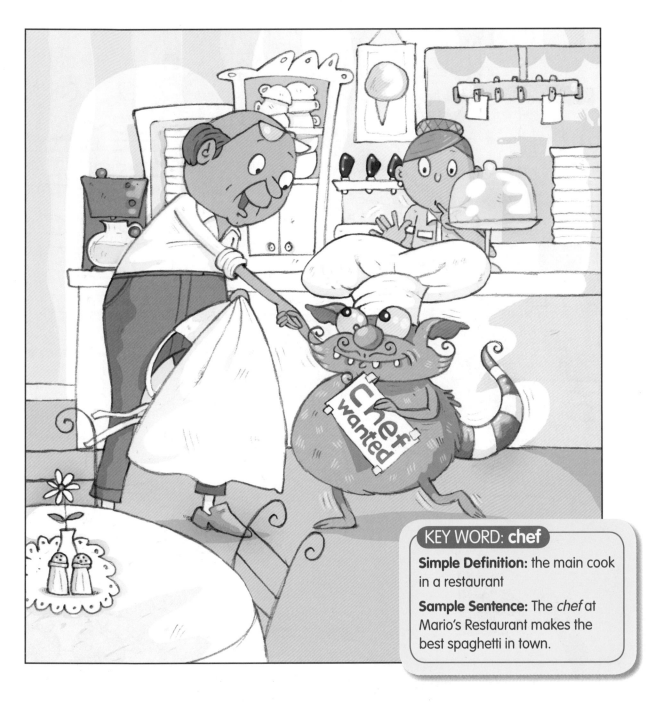

KEY WORD: **chef**

Simple Definition: the main cook in a restaurant

Sample Sentence: The *chef* at Mario's Restaurant makes the best spaghetti in town.

"I can cook," said a hairy purple monster with a striped tail.

Mr. Dibble had hoped to find a human **chef**.

But a monster chef would have to do.

"You're hired!" said Mr. Dibble.

Mr. Dibble took the monster to the kitchen.
The monster looked around and roared with joy.
"I hope he works out," said Mr. Dibble to himself.

KEY WORD: **menu**

Simple Definition: a list of foods served in a restaurant

Sample Sentence: We read the *menu*, and all the food sounded super tasty.

After a while, the very first customer arrived. Her name was Fifi Frank and she was a very fussy eater. She studied the **menu** for a long time. "I'll have the soup," she said.

"Can you make soup?" Mr. Dibble asked the monster.

"Absolutely! I have an old family **recipe**," the monster replied.

KEY WORD: boil

Simple Definition: to heat something until it starts to bubble

Sample Sentence: You need to *boil* the water before you add the rice.

The monster put a big pot on the stove. He filled it with orange juice. Soon the juice began to **boil**.

The monster tossed cherries, cheese, and a donut into the pot. He threw in ham, potato chips, and a scoop of strawberry ice cream.

KEY WORD: **pinch**

Simple Definition: a small amount of something

Sample Sentence: The recipe asked for lots of butter and a *pinch* of salt.

The monster tasted the soup. It was almost ready. Now, for the final touches. He added a few drops of honey and just a **pinch** of salt.

KEY WORD: ingredients

Simple Definition: foods and spices used in a recipe

Sample Sentence: Peanut butter, jelly, and bread are the *ingredients* of my favorite sandwich.

When the soup was ready, Mr. Dibble couldn't believe his eyes. He had never seen soup with such strange **ingredients**. But there was no time to waste. He rushed it right out to Fifi Frank.

Fifi stared at her soup for a long, long time.
Finally, she tasted it and said. . .

"This soup is totally **scrumptious**!" Then she added, "I'm going to tell all my friends to come and try it!"

12

Soon the restaurant was packed with people. The customers loved the soup. Mr. Dibble loved the customers. And what did the monster love? His job and brand-new **apron**!

Meaning Match

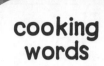

cooking words

Listen to the definition. Then go to the WORD CHEST and find a vocabulary word that matches it.

1 foods and spices used in a recipe

2 something you wear to protect your clothes when you are cooking

3 very delicious

4 a small amount of something

5 the main cook in a restaurant

6 to heat something until it starts to bubble

7 instructions for cooking food

8 a list of foods served in a restaurant

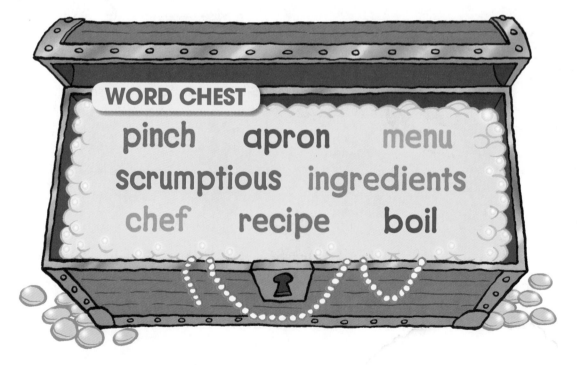

WORD CHEST

pinch   apron   menu
scrumptious   ingredients
chef   recipe   boil

14

Vocabulary Fill-ins

Listen to the sentence. Then go to the WORD BOX and find the best word to fill in the blank.

WORD BOX

chef	menu	ingredients	boil
recipe	apron	scrumptious	pinch

1. Be sure to put on an _____ so you won't get your clothes dirty.

2. My mother waited for the water to _____, then she dropped in the eggs.

3. Jenny says her _____ for brownies is top secret.

4. The Tiptop Diner has a large _____, with many different foods to choose from.

5. The restaurant's _____ wears a tall white hat.

6. Jermaine said it was the most _____ pie he had ever tasted.

7. The pizza tasted great because all the _____ were so fresh.

8. Amber sprinkled a little pepper, and Alice added a _____ of salt.

Answers: 1. apron 2. boil 3. recipe 4. menu 5. chef 6. scrumptious 7. ingredients 8. pinch

Vocabulary Questions

Listen to each question. Think about it. Then answer.

1. Would you like to be a **chef** when you grow up? Where would you work?

2. Create a **menu** for your favorite meal. What is the main course? What is for dessert?

3. Would you rather eat something with a **pinch** of salt or a pile of salt? Why?

4. If someone makes water **boil**, it is very hot. Why is it dangerous to get too close to boiling water?

5. Make up a **recipe** for pizza. What can you add to make it extra special?

6. What foods do you think taste totally **scrumptious**? Make a list.

7. Sometimes **aprons** have messages on them. What would you like your **apron** to say?

8. Imagine something called "super soup." What would its **ingredients** be?

Extra: Can you think of some more cooking words? Make a list.